SUSANNE BUDDENBERG / THOMAS HENSELER

A City Divided

CHRONICLES

avant-verlag

The comic book "Berlin – A City Divided" is based on actual events.

With the support of
The Federal Foundation for the Reappraisal of the SED Dictatorship

BUNDESSTIFTUNG
  AUFARBEITUNG

Scenario and gray tones: Susanne Buddenberg
Scenario and drawings: Thomas Henseler
Zoom und Tinte Buddenberg und Henseler GbR

Editor: Markus Pieper

Historical texts: Dr. Christian Halbrock
Historical consultant: Dr. Maria Nooke – Berlin Wall Memorial

English translation: Rick Minnich
Typesetting and graphic design: Andreas Rupprecht
Photos 1986/1987: Detlef Matthes
Photos 2012: Anna Schmelz

Publisher: Johann Ulrich
avant-verlag / Weichselplatz 3–4 / 12045 Berlin
info@avant-verlag.de
www.avant-verlag.de
facebook.com/avant-verlag

ISBN 978-3-939080-75-6
Second edition, 2013

Table of Contents

S-BAHN TICKET TO WEST BERLIN FROM AUGUST 16, 1961

REGINA ZYWIETZ: How the Wall Nearly Put an End to My High School Career

EAST BERLIN, FRIEDRICHSTRASSE RAILWAY STATION, AUGUST 16, 1961

[Banner on train station:
Neues Deutschland proclaims: A Dark Day for Warmongers]

REGINA ZYWIETZ (19). The East Berliner goes to high school in the West and will be taking her finals soon.

But the borders have been closed for the past 4 days.

Meeting my teachers who want to help me flee to West Berlin.

DR. WELLMER

MR. MÜNZEL

DR. RINTELEN

We act like complete strangers and don't exchange a single word.

One ticket to West Berlin.

That's 20 pfennigs.

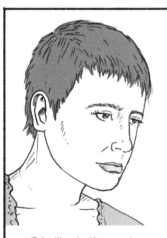

It's like in the movies: I'm the leading actress and a spectator rolled into one.

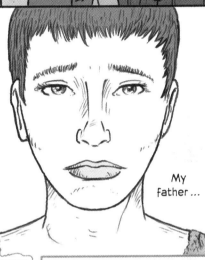

My father ...

... was a Protestant minister in East Berlin. That automatically made us enemies of the "workers' and peasants' state."

That's why I was deemed "politically unreliable" and denied admission to an East Berlin secondary school despite my good grades.

9

The West Berlin Senate established special classes for students who had fled from the East or been rejected there. One of these was at the Bertha von Suttner School in Reinickendorf, where I'd been going since 1955.

The East classes were a motley crew of ragged characters of all ages from the entire GDR.

Many things were different here.

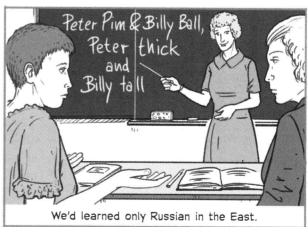

We'd learned only Russian in the East.

In the GDR, we were supposed to regurgitate the prevailing views in class. But here they suddenly expected us to have our own opinions about everything.

Some of my classmates lived in West Berlin. But I always rode across the sector border back to East Berlin.

EAST BERLIN: GRELLSTRASSE 55

We had already completed our written exams. During the summer holidays, I prepared for the oral exams, which were supposed to take place in September 1961.

Afterwards I wanted to study German Literature at the FU*, where I had already been accepted.

* FU: Free University in West Berlin

12

I was home alone. Everyone else in my family was out of town. My older brothers were in the West, in Hamburg.

My parents were with my younger brother in the East, on the Island of Rügen.

Because my father was a minister, we were one of the few families with a telephone.

RING

SUNDAY, AUGUST 13, 1961

They closed the borders this morning!

The news from my East Berlin classmate Katja woke me with a start.

Well, it's not the first time.* They were closed back in '53, too. But not for long.

After all, we're a Four-Power city! The Americans, the English and the French will never put up with this!

WEST BERLIN   EAST BERLIN

* The borders were closed following the bloody suppression of the national uprising in the GDR on June 17, 1953. They were re-opened a few weeks later.

13

I went with some of my classmates from the East to see what was going on.

There were no more loopholes. We were fenced in.

They were closing off the gateway to the West.

[Banner:
Socialism shall triumph!
We are the mightier!]

It was impossible to reach anyone in my family.

DING-DONG

ZYWIETZ

My West Berlin classmate PETER could still enter
East Berlin with his ID card at his own risk.*

* After August 24, 1961, West Berliners could no longer do this.

15

My teachers from the Bertha von Suttner School sent Peter with an offer to help me flee.

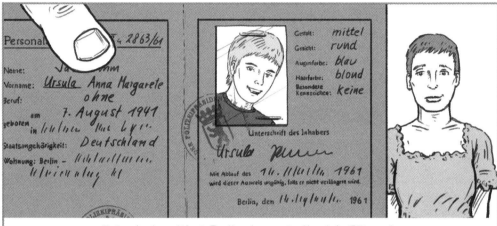

Peter had my West Berlin classmate Ursula's ID card.
We had the same crew cuts but different colored eyes and hair.
I was to cross the border as her.

Peter gave me the West money for my ticket and left. I was supposed to meet my teachers Dr. Wellmer, Dr. Rintelen and Mr. Münzel at the newspaper stand at the Friedrichstrasse station at 5 p.m.

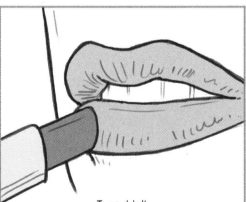

I couldn't take anything with me: no family pictures, no papers, nothing that might betray me. I put on some lipstick and my best clothes in order to pass as a westerner. All I took with me was a wicker basket made in Italy.

I shut the door behind me and left the house without saying goodbye to anyone.

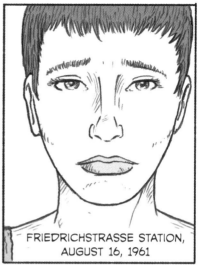

FRIEDRICHSTRASSE STATION, AUGUST 16, 1961

Move along.

ID card!

When's the next train?

My teachers distract the border guard to prevent him from inspecting my photo too closely.

Check the departure schedule!

Are you carrying any East German currency?

No.

The 3rd inspection by the platform staircase.

18

We reach the platform as the train is pulling out of the station.

It seems like an eternity until the next train arrives.

We don't stay in a group but spread out along the platform.

The station is swarming with soldiers.

A solider approaches me.

He takes a close look at my face ...

... as though he knows who I am.

I recognize him imme-diately.

He was one of my father's confirmands.

The next train departs at last!

BERLIN - FRIEDRICHSTRASS

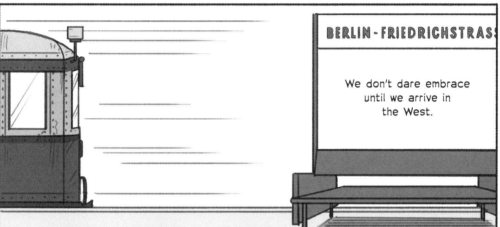

BERLIN - FRIEDRICHSTRASS

We don't dare embrace
until we arrive in
the West.

My overwhelming joy
at my successful flight is
tainted by guilt and concern
about my parents and my
younger brother.
I won't see them again
for the next five years.

I arrive in the West with
only the clothes on my back.
I live with my English
teacher at first.
The teachers at our school
take up a collection for
the students who fled
from the East.
I pass my final exams.

My teachers
left a lasting impression
on me. They felt responsible
for me and my future and
took tremendous risks
without ever expecting
anything in return.
That's why I decide
to become a
teacher
myself.

THE END

The four
sectors of Berlin

Walter Ulbricht

The GDR flag

Nikita Khrushchev

Germany and Berlin Are Divided

The construction of the Berlin Wall on August 13, 1961, which nearly prevented Regina Zywietz from taking her final exams, was the culmination of the dramatic developments of the previous sixteen years. After World War II, Germany was divided into four zones of occupation: the USA, Great Britain and France occupied the three western zones and the USSR the one "East Zone." In the three western zones, which later became the Federal Republic of Germany, western-style parliamentary democracy was established. In the eastern zone, however, the USSR – with the support of the monopolistic Socialist Unity Party (SED) under the leadership of Walter Ulbricht – established a dictatorship along the lines of the other Soviet-controlled Eastern Bloc countries. Freedom of assembly, freedom of association, and freedom of the press were abolished. The SED established the secret police ("Stasi") in 1950, and granted it far-reaching authority to crush all forms of protest. The seemingly omniscient Stasi intimidated East German society, and readily enforced its will with random arrests. Anyone who refused to tow the line in the new socialist system ran a great risk and could rarely count on the support of others.

At the same time, the government of the German Democratic Republic (GDR), as the Soviet Zone was called beginning in October 1949, continued to divide the country. In May 1952, it established a five-kilometer wide restricted zone along the border to the Federal Republic, and clamped down on GDR citizens who traveled to the West to work or study. Unchecked border crossings between East and West Germany were stopped.

In Berlin, the situation was somewhat different. Just as Germany was divided into four occupation zones, Berlin was also divided into four sectors. Because Berlin was located in the Soviet zone, the three western-controlled sectors of West Berlin were in the middle of the GDR. Many East Berliners and residents of the surrounding areas in the GDR continued to work in West Berlin. Numerous pupils and students from the East attended schools in the western part of the city. Conversely, other students, teachers, doctors, lecturers and professors lived in the western sectors and traveled to East Berlin with the S-Bahn, which still connected East and West. But here the SED continued its efforts to divide the city.

During the late-1950s, the situation in and around Berlin escalated. In the so-called "Berlin Ultimatum" of 1958, Nikita Khrushchev, Soviet party leader and head of state, demanded that the western part of the city be transformed into an "autonomous political entity." The western allies were unwilling to do this, however, because inevitably it would have meant abandoning West Berlin. A failed summit conference in Paris in May 1960 further exacerbated the situation. All this was part of the political scheming of the leaders in Moscow and East Berlin, who were becoming increasingly concerned about West Berlin, which they considered a "thorn in the flesh of the GDR." With its democratic society and western products, West Berlin was situated in the middle of the GDR and was still fairly easy to reach from the East. Because radio and television stations broadcast critical reports from here, the GDR could hardly shield itself from the western lifestyle and democratic ideas. An increasing number of East Germans were also turning their backs on socialism and fleeing across the open border into West Berlin. Domestic political repressions such as the forced agrarian collectivization led to a rapid increase in the number of refugees. Between 1949 and 1961, an estimated 2.7 million people fled the GDR.

Shortly before Regina Zywietz's final exams, at 1 a.m. on August 13, 1961, Walter Ulbricht gave orders to seal off the city's border. On the morning of August 13th, para-military combat group formations, the German Border Police, and East German People's Police joined forces to seal off the border. During the ensuing days and weeks, a wall was quickly constructed out of barbed-wire barriers, gates and concrete slabs. Berlin and Germany were divided, and thousands of friends and families were separated. West Berlin became a walled in island in the middle of the GDR, where anyone who tried to cross the border into the western part of the city risked coming into the crosshairs of border guards with a "shoot-to-kill order" …

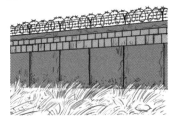

First generation
Berlin Wall

ON LOCATION

The **FRIEDRICHSTRASSE RAILWAY STATION** was completely renovated and remodeled after the fall of the Berlin Wall. The **TRÄNENPALAST** (Palace of Tears) still stands in the forecourt. During GDR times, this was the border crossing departure hall. Today it houses the permanent exhibition "Border Experiences – Everyday Life in Divided Germany."

www.hdg.de/berlin

▶ **Friedrichstrasse Railway Station**

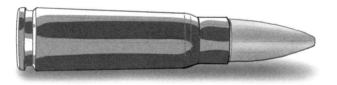

BULLET 7.62 X 39 MM CALIBER

URSULA MALCHOW: The Hospital by the Wall

WEST BERLIN, LATE-SUMMER 1961:
THE LAZARUS HOSPITAL AT
BERNAUER STRASSE 114-118

We've been living and
working here since 1958.

My husband
GÜNTER works as
a male nurse.

I bring the patients
their meals.

We live with our children on the mezzanine floor next to the emergency room.

Across the street begins East Berlin, another country, the GDR.

The buildings there belong to the East.
The exits to the West are being sealed
off one by one.

Whenever we notice people fleeing,
we try to act normal
so the border guards don't
become suspicious.

Time and time again people desperately try to escape into the West.

Some flee over the roof-tops, the border guards in hot pursuit.

GDR border guards try to pull others back up into the East while West Berliners try to pull them down into the West.

The West Berlin police try to protect those on the run.

Some escapees rappel on bed sheets tied together.

Others jump into the fire department's rescue nets.

snap

The sheets often tear ...

... or refugees fall and hurt themselves.

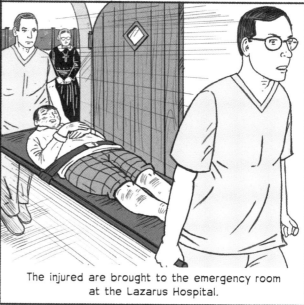

The injured are brought to the emergency room at the Lazarus Hospital.

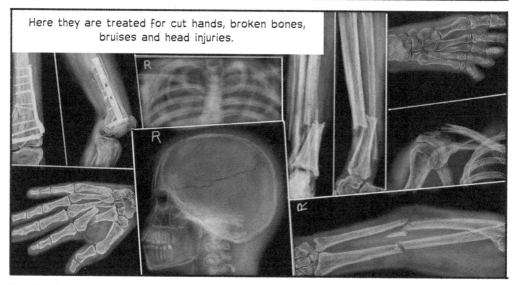

Here they are treated for cut hands, broken bones, bruises and head injuries.

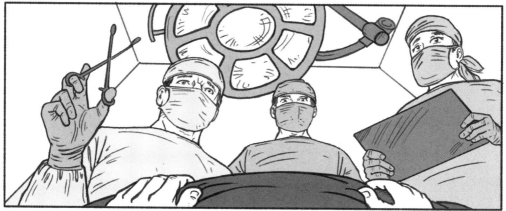

But the patients don't have a minute's rest here..

Many West Berliners come here to vent their outrage at the GDR regime.

The Wall becomes a tourist attraction where people honk in protest.

We form a human chain and demonstrate against the ongoing disturbances.

Im Bereich de Krankenhaus nicht hupe

Later a no honking sign is posted.

Dem Gründer
des
Lazarus-Hauses
Wilhelm Boegehold

SOPHIEN PARISH CEMETERY, EAST BERLIN

FREEZE! DON'T MOVE!

When shots are fired on the other side, they often ricochet off the emergency room wall.

RATATATATAT

The West Berlin police search the grounds with floodlights to secure the bullet casings as evidence.

This often leads to conflicts with our head physician.

You can search for projectiles tomorrow. Our patients need their rest now.

Leave the grounds.

The emergency room is open around the clock for escapees and casualties.

SEPTEMBER 4, 1962, 2:20 P.M. EMERGENCY ROOM.
Günter is on duty.

Bullets are echoing from the cemetery.

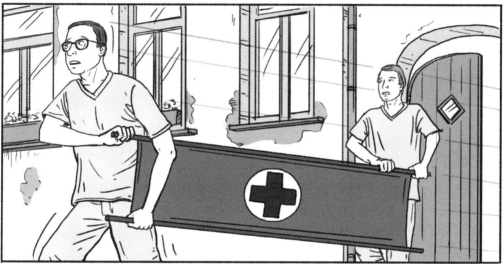

KILLERS!!

What happened?

Today is visitation day at the Sophien parish cemetery. From 2–6 p.m., East Berliners are allowed to visit their loved ones' graves under the supervision of border guards.

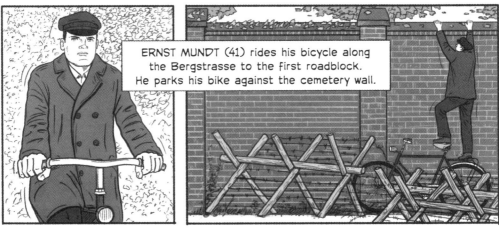

ERNST MUNDT (41) rides his bicycle along the Bergstrasse to the first roadblock. He parks his bike against the cemetery wall.

WEST   EAST

Don't be
a fool!
Get down!

No way!

Ernst Mundt wanted to flee to his
mother in West Berlin. But only
his hat made it to the West.

Ernst Mundt is the fifth fatality
in the Bernauer Strasse.
136 people will end up losing their
lives along the Berlin Wall.

THE END

Death at the Border

The Wall tore apart entire families

[Riding the U-Bahn and S-Bahn throughout Berlin]

During the months and years following the construction of the Wall, what many had considered impossible was apparently becoming horrible reality. An entire city was systematically divided: streets, waterways, underground and S-Bahn connections were all severed. The sealing of the border brought tremendous suffering upon countless families. If one half lived in the other part of Germany, there was no hope of being able to meet again in the foreseeable future. And it was completely unclear whether this situation would ever change. Parents and children, siblings, grandparents and grandchildren, couples, friends, classmates and colleagues were all separated from one another. Thousands of people lost their job, property or apartment in the other part of the country. No one could evade the dictatorship in East Germany and begin a self-determined life in the West. The borders were sealed.

West Berlin was completely cut off from the surrounding areas. Its only connection to the Federal Republic was via three automobile and railway transit corridors and by air. Anyone who was at risk of being arrested while in transit through the GDR had to fly in and out of Berlin on the airlines operated by the Allies. Extensive subsidy and aid programs guaranteed the survival of what had become an island half-city. Extra Berlin allowances were implemented to discourage companies from relocating to West Germany. Because the GDR continued to operate the S-Bahn in the western part of the city, West Berliners boycotted it after the construction of the Wall, and greatly extended the U-Bahn system in the western half of the city.

Over time, the border fortifications in East Berlin were constantly upgraded and perfected. Buildings adjacent to the eastern side of the border were vacated and often demolished to prevent further escapes and to create a "shooting corridor." One trouble spot was Bernauer Strasse between the districts Mitte (East) and Wedding (West), where the Lazarus Hospital is located. Here the Wall divided a densely-built street into an eastern and a western section. From September 25-26,1961, the residents on the east side of Bernauer Strasse, whose sidewalk belonged to the West, were evicted with military precision. First the windows facing the West were walled up. Then, in 1962, the demolition of the rear buildings began, followed by the full-fledged demolition of the front buildings down to the outer walls of the ground floor in 1965. These were initially used as provisional border fortifications, and were integrated into the border wall – the second of the two walls, which was located closest to West Berlin. In order to make a good impression on the West, the eastern buildings visible from the west side of the Wall were renovated and beautified beginning in the mid-1980s. But behind this facade, the buildings continued

Walled up windows in Bernauer Strasse

their inexorable decay. Vacated apartments near the border were rented out only to "reliable" citizens – ideally to party comrades.

On the east side, several cemeteries near the border were accessible only with a "border authorisation permit." The East Berlin magistrate later extended the forbidden areas and transferred graves to create an unrestricted view. Such was the case at the Sophien parish cemetery across from the Lazarus Hospital on Bernauer Strasse.

Getting anywhere near the Wall became increasingly difficult. Those who actually made it to the border fortifications risked their lives trying to cross into the West. During the twenty-eight years that the Wall divided Berlin, at least 136 people lost their lives here, including 98 defectors. They were either shot or injured while trying to escape or took their own lives when their escape attempts turned sour. Thirty people who were not even trying to escape died in accidents or were accidentally shot in the border area. Eight GDR border guards also lost their lives.

The following story recalls the spectacular escape of an entire family in 1965 …

DEM UNBEKANNTEN OPFER DER SCHANDMAUER
+ 4.9.1962

[For the unknown victim of the Wall of Shame]

Memorial plaque for the then unknown Ernst Mundt in Bernauer Strasse

ON LOCATION

The Lazarus Hospital is still located at Bernauer Strasse 114-118. A visit to the **BERLIN WALL MEMORIAL** is highly recommended. The large open-air exhibition in the former death strip features border fortifications and a presentation about German division. Also located on the grounds are the **VISITOR CENTER AND DOCUMENTATION CENTER** with a viewing tower and exhibition about the Berlin Wall, as well as the **CHAPEL OF RECONCILIATION**.

At the nearby S-Bahn station **NORDBAHNHOF**, the exhibition "Border Stations and Ghost Stations in Divided Berlin" offers visitors a look at how the construction of the Wall affected the city's traffic system. It also includes documents of former "ghost stations."

www.berliner-mauer-gedenkstaette.de

▶ **Tram stop**
  Gedenkstätte Berliner Mauer
▶ **S-Bahn station Nordbahnhof**
▶ **U-Bahn station Naturkundemuseum**
▶ **U-Bahn station Bernauer Strasse**

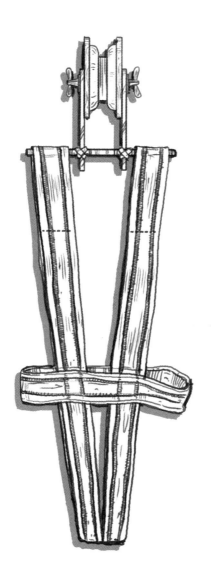

HANDMADE PULLEY WITH SHOULDER STRAP

THE HOLZAPFEL FAMILY: Ziplining over the Wall

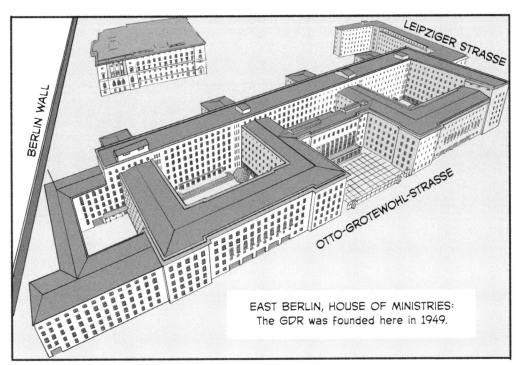

LEIPZIGER STRASSE

BERLIN WALL

OTTO-GROTEWOHL-STRASSE

EAST BERLIN, HOUSE OF MINISTRIES:
The GDR was founded here in 1949.

JULY 28, 1965: LEIPZIGER STRASSE, EMPLOYEE ENTRANCE

HEINZ HOLZAPFEL from Leipzig

The 34-year-old industrial economist and production scheduler is here for a bi-monthly meeting. He has lost his faith in socialism.

The West is far superior to the "workers' and peasants' state." No empty slogans can hide this any longer.

Today he wants to flee the GDR with his wife JUTTA and their son GÜNTER (9).

He has planned every last detail of their flight. He has organized passes for him and his wife. Children accompanied by their parents do not need one.

The family must remain inside the building until closing time at 5 o'clock.
They go unnoticed among the 6,000 employees and privileged functionaries in the
building, which houses numerous shops and amenities for its workforce.

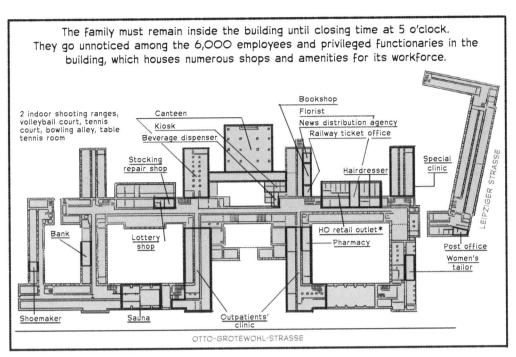

- 2 indoor shooting ranges, volleyball court, tennis court, bowling alley, table tennis room
- Canteen
- Kiosk
- Beverage dispenser
- Stocking repair shop
- Bookshop
- Florist
- News distribution agency
- Railway ticket office
- Hairdresser
- Special clinic
- LEIPZIGER STRASSE
- Bank
- Lottery shop
- HO retail outlet*
- Pharmacy
- Post office
- Women's tailor
- Shoemaker
- Sauna
- Outpatients' clinic

OTTO-GROTEWOHL-STRASSE

* HO = state retail agency

5:05 P.M.: Closing time in the ministry.
All the employees leave the building.

RESTROOM
CLOSED.
Please use
one at end of
corridor. →

The family hides in the restroom.
Heinz Holzapfel hung the sign
on the door and bolted
it from the inside.

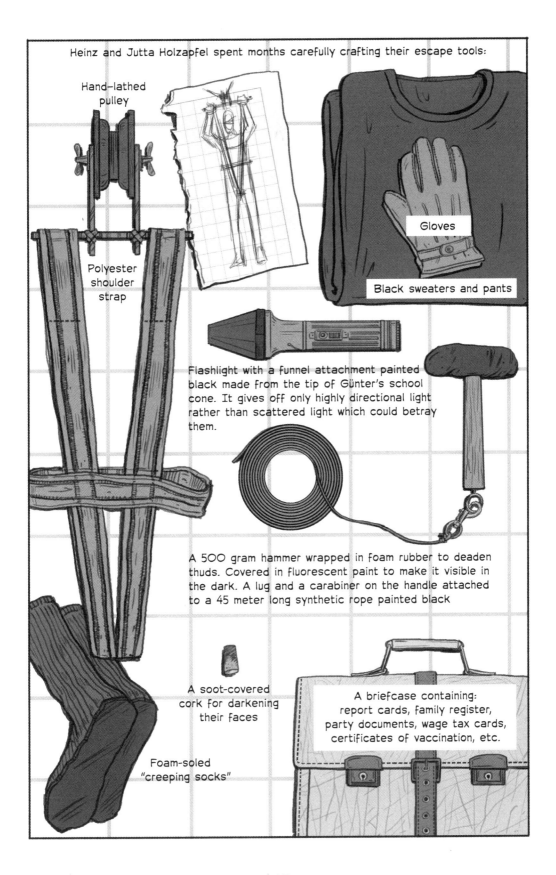

Heinz and Jutta Holzapfel spent months carefully crafting their escape tools:

Hand–lathed pulley

Polyester shoulder strap

Gloves

Black sweaters and pants

Flashlight with a funnel attachment painted black made from the tip of Günter's school cone. It gives off only highly directional light rather than scattered light which could betray them.

A 500 gram hammer wrapped in foam rubber to deaden thuds. Covered in fluorescent paint to make it visible in the dark. A lug and a carabiner on the handle attached to a 45 meter long synthetic rope painted black

A soot-covered cork for darkening their faces

A briefcase containing: report cards, family register, party documents, wage tax cards, certificates of vaccination, etc.

Foam-soled "creeping socks"

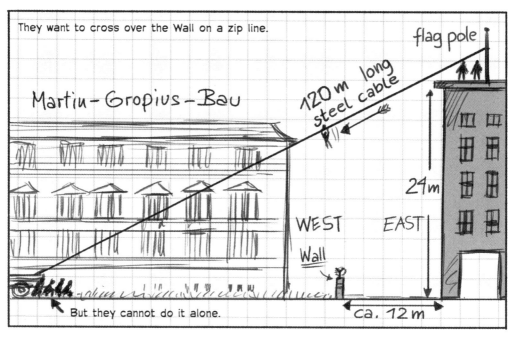

They want to cross over the Wall on a zip line.

Martin-Gropius-Bau

flag pole

120 m long steel cable

24 m

WEST   EAST

Wall

ca. 12 m

But they cannot do it alone.

Four family members from the West are helping them:

KURT HOLZAPFEL
From Mainz –
Heinz' brother

HERMANN SCHMIDT
from Nuremberg –
Heinz' brother-in-law

GERHARD LINDNER and   KURT LINDNER from Burgheim – Jutta's brothers

And what if they shoot?

They won't shoot toward the roof because no one will see us there.

And if we're careful, they won't see the zip line either.

9:45 P.M.

It starts to rain.

The entire time a Soviet air surveillance lookout on the rooftop closely observes them.

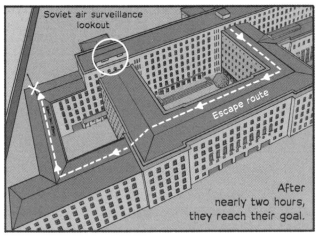

Soviet air surveillance lookout

Escape route

After nearly two hours, they reach their goal.

They blacken their faces.

It all comes down to the hammer throw.

A helper removes the carabiner with the synthetic rope from the hammer.

The synthetic rope is attached to an 8 mm thick steel cable.

Jutta and Heinz pull the heavy cable to the rooftop and attach it to the flag pole.

Signal to the helpers that the cable can be pulled taut.

The cable is hanging too taut over the roof edge.

Heinz Holzapfel has to lift it up over his shoulder to form a gap between the cable and the roof edge.

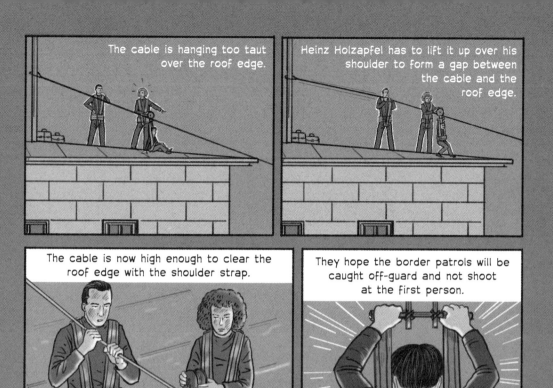

The cable is now high enough to clear the roof edge with the shoulder strap.

They hope the border patrols will be caught off-guard and not shoot at the first person.

Jutta Holzapfel is next.

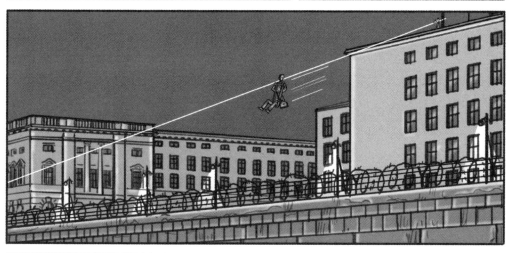

Heinz Holzapfel held up the cable for his wife and son. Now no one is there to do the same for him.

He cannot get past the roof edge.

The cable does not budge a single millimeter.

The path to freedom appears just out of reach.

The helpers are at a loss and don't know what to do ...

You've got to loosen the cable!

It takes an entire hour to get to the root of the problem.

Heinz Holzapfel can now slide the cable up the flag pole.

The path is clear.

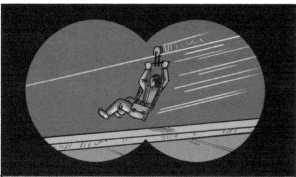

The Soviet guard thinks the GDR secret police are trying to sneak their own agents into the West, so he does not sound the alarm.

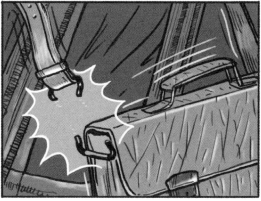

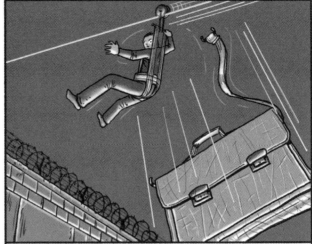

The briefcase with the various documents lands in the GDR border area. The East German secret police quickly discover who fled.

But the Holzapfel family never regret their flight.

THE END

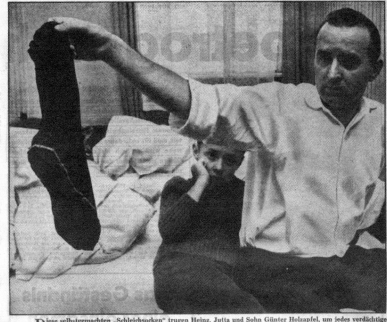

Punkt Mitternacht rollte der kleine Günter mutig in einer Seilschlinge auf dem 140 Meter langen Stahlseil in den 25 Meter tiefen Abgrund.

Dann folgte die Frau. „Ich sah unter mir den Todesstreifen. Als ich die Mauer sah, dachte ich : Jetzt bist du gerettet!"

Als letzter rollte der Vater in die Freiheit — mit Rollen, die eine VEB-Schlosserei nach den Plänen Holzapfels angefertigt hatte.

In einem Hotel trank man erst mal zur Beruhigung einen Kognak. Dann ging es in die Betten. Übernachtung und Frühstück waren gratis.

Die Helfer waren noch kühn genug, das Fluchtseil teilweise zusammenzuwickeln und auf die Mauerkrone zu legen. Erst Stunden später wurde es von der Vopo entdeckt.

Einsicht

Heinz Holzapfel vermag kaum auszudrücken, wie glücklich er sich fühlt. „Wenn ich noch daran denke, wie wir im strömenden Regen auf dem Dach langkrochen, aus einer Dachluke drang Licht und Stimmengewirr — offenbar hausten dort Grenzwächter. Aber wir mußten das Risiko eingehen."

Denn die Leipziger Familie konnte die Zustände in der Zone nicht länger ertragen. „Ich mußte einsehen, daß die kommunistische Ideologie in den Lehrbüchern ganz anders aufgeht als in der Praxis." Das sagt immerhin ein Mann, der jahrelang seinen Kollegen die Beschlüsse des SED-Zentralkomitees erläutern mußte.

Denn jahrelang galt Heinz Holzapfel als Musterknabe in der Zone: Als gelernter Tischler war er zur kasernierten Volkspolizei gegangen und hatte eine Offiziersschule besucht. Mit Hilfe von Stipendien machte er das Abitur und studierte vier Jahre an der Karl-Marx-Universität.

„Ich war Überzeugungskommunist!" gesteht heute der ehemalige SED-Funktionär. Aber seit dem Bau der Sperrmauer bekam er er Zweifel, die größer und größer wurden, bis er sich schließlich zur Flucht entschloß.

Heinz Holzapfel blickt hoffnungsvoll in die Zukunft: In Süddeutschland will er eine eigene Existenz aufbauen. Grundlage: zwei Patente, die er schon vor einiger Zeit in West-Berlin anmelden ließ.

Sprung aus den Wolken

Mit diesem Buch über Fallschirmspringer bereitete Vater Holzapfel seinen Sohn auf das gefährliche Unternehmen vor.

Nach geglückter Flucht: Ein Grenzpolizist mit geschultertem Gewehr zieht das Drahtseil über die Mauer nach Osten.

Erstes gemeinsames Frühstück auf West-Berliner Gebiet: Jetzt kann Familie Holzapfel Beruhigungspillen und die ganze Aufregung vergessen.

Diese selbstgemachten „Schleichsocken" trugen Heinz, Jutta und Sohn Günter Holzapfel, um jedes verdächtige Geräusch auf dem Dach vom „Haus der Ministerien" zu vermeiden. Sie hatten tatsächlich an alles gedacht.

* See translation of newspaper article on page 95

Walled In

Watchtower
from the 1970s

The Wall had already been in place for four years when the Holz-apfel family made their escape. GDR propaganda referred to the Wall as the "Anti-Fascist Bulwark" – as though the East had to protect itself against a new wave of fascism from West Germany. At the same time, however, the GDR leadership was keenly aware of how necessary it was to tightly seal the borders to stop the country's "hemorrhaging" from the massive flow of refugees to the West.

Over the years, the implementation of firearms, controls in the run up to the Wall, automobile barrier trenches, observation towers and dog runs made the Wall a virtually insurmountable obstacle. But the human desire to live in freedom remained un-vanquished. As the means of confinement continued to be perfect-ed, he escape attempts became increasingly daring and inven-tive. Between 1961 and 1989, the year the Wall fell, 5,075 people escaped through the border installations in Berlin. They fled over or under the Wall, by land, water or air. Some attempted to break through the Wall with diesel locomotives or concrete-reinforced trucks. Others tried to escape through unsecured sewer pipes, U-Bahn tunnels, self-dug tunnels or by swimming across the Spree River. Still others tried to fly out of the GDR in homemade hot-air balloons or light aircraft. A number of defectors managed to escape using falsified papers or with an exit visa arranged by helpers in the West. Some hid in automobile trunks or trains.

During the 1970s, the SED (Sozialistische Einheitspartei Deutsch-land = Socialist Unity Party of Germany: The ruling party in the German Democratic Republic/GDR) once again stepped up its efforts to make the Wall even more impermeable. The new focus was on spotting and detaining potential escapees in the run up to the Wall.

One of the State Security's (Stasi) key tasks was to find out if someone intended to flee the GDR. Such persons could then be stopped before they even reached the border area. The Stasi re-ceived a great deal of its information from so-called "unofficial collaborators" or IMs (abbreviation of "inoffizieller Mitarbeiter" = unofficial collaborator) from a suspect's private or work circles. In 1989, a total of 189,000 IMs were spying for the Stasi (of a nation-al population of 16 million). For this reason, it could be extremely risky to discuss escape plans with any friends or acquaintances who were not directly involved. A long prison sentence awaited those whose escape plans were exposed.

Security conferences and resolutions "for the increased secu-rity of the interior of the state frontier" were supposed to prevent escapes through the Wall. Party veterans and volunteer street wardens and border troop helpers patrolled the neighboring streets during particularly "dangerous situations" such as the an-niversary of the construction of the Wall or the anniversary of the founding of the GDR on October 7th. In foggy or smoggy weather, the People's Police reinforced the border troops.

[Ministry for
State Security]

Anyone who came too close to the Wall was considered suspicious. Reckless behavior, a wave toward the West or a nighttime walk could have fatal consequences. Photographing the border fortifications was strictly prohibited …

[Stop! Frontier border! No passing or photography permitted!]

ON LOCATION

The Federal Ministry of Finance now occupies the former **House of Ministries** at Wilhelmstrasse 97. The Ministry's visitor service offers tours to organized groups upon prior arrangement. A mural from GDR times as well as the monument to the national uprising on June 17, 1953 are visible from the front of the building on Leipziger Strasse.

www.bundesfinanzministerium.de/EN

▶ **S- and U-Bahn station Potsdamer Platz**
▶ **U-Bahn station Mohrenstrasse**
▶ **Bus stop Abgeordnetenhaus (House of Representatives)**

The former Allied border crossing **CHECKPOINT CHARLIE** is located at the nearby intersection of Zimmerstrasse and Friedrichstrasse:

The **WALL MUSEUM** Haus am Checkpoint Charlie at Friedrichstrasse 43-45 features exhibits about the division of Berlin and escapes from the GDR.

www.mauermuseum.de/english

A few steps further down the road at Zimmerstrasse 90 is the **BILDUNGSZENTRUM DES BUNDESBEAUFTRAGTEN FÜR DIE STASI-UNTERLAGEN** (Educational Center of the Federal Commissioner for the Stasi Files), where the permanent exhibit "Stasi – Exhibition on the GDR State Security" is on display.

www.bstu.de

If you continue eastward down Zimmerstrasse, you will find two **MEMORIALS** just past Friedrichstrasse: at the corner of Zimmerstrasse and Charlottenstrasse, a stele pays tribute to Peter Fechter, who bled to death in the death strip while attempting to scale the Wall in 1962. At Jerusalemer Strasse, you can find information about a 20-year-old sergeant from the GDR border troops who lost his life while trying to escape through a tunnel in 1962.

▶ **U-Bahn station Kochstrasse**

"EXA 1B" MODEL FROM VEB CERTO KAMERAWERK DRESDEN

DETLEF MATTHES: The Other Side

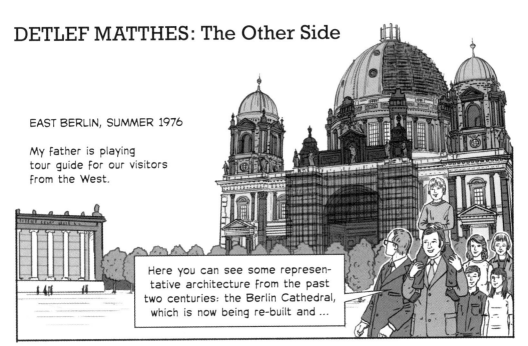

EAST BERLIN, SUMMER 1976

My father is playing tour guide for our visitors from the West.

Here you can see some representative architecture from the past two centuries: the Berlin Cathedral, which is now being re-built and ...

... the new landmark of East Berlin – the recently opened "Palace of the Republic."

The family strolls along the boulevard "Unter den Linden."

Here's the magnificent embassy of the USSR.

Dad ...

Hmm?

... what's that white thing over there?

That's the Wall.

The Wall?

What's West Berlin?

The other part of Berlin.

Yes, and behind it is West Berlin.

The "other part" of Berlin was terra incognita for me. Our maps showed it as undeveloped territory.

Years later, this white spot on the map was still on my mind.
What did it really look like there?

AT HOME
IN BIESENTHAL
(GDR).

33 KM
FROM BERLIN

I collect postcards of
West Berlin from our relatives
in the West. They make me even
more curious.

For confirmation I got an
"Exa 1b" camera.

Now I could take pictures myself.

Click!

The pictures we see of the West Berlin side of the Wall look completely different from the East. Here you can't get anywhere near the border.

THERE'S NOTHING
TO SEE HERE!
KEEP MOVING!

Over time, I learn to walk along the Wall inconspicuously. I act like I live nearby and am headed somewhere.

Click!

Whenever I'm out and about in strange courtyards near the Wall, I never know
if border guards might be patrolling the area.

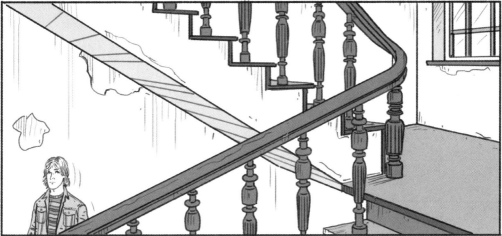

The Wall is painted white to make it easier to see escapees.
There's not enough paint leftover for the crumbling facades in the East.

LEIPZIGER STRASSE

These high-rises offer the best views of the West.

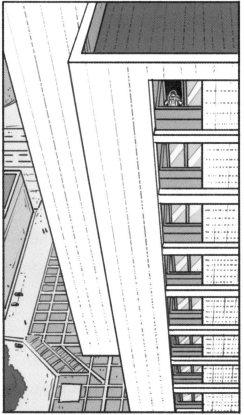

AXEL SPRINGER PUBLISHING HOUSE, WEST BERLIN

Click!

I always try to get a compartment of my own in the S-Bahn, and wait for an opportunity to take pictures. Usually I have about 10 rolls of film with me.

Click!

Back home in Biesenthal a surprise awaits me.

OR WO FACHGESCHÄFT FOTO·FILM

Mr. Matthes, you can't take pictures of border fortifications! That's strictly prohibited!

He keeps the prints but lets me take the negatives.

I take a photography course at my vocational school.

Now I can make prints at home whenever I want.

WHITSUN 1987:

In West Berlin, a rock concert celebrating the city's 750th anniversary takes place right in front of the Wall by the Reichstag. Over three days, 70,000 fans come to see New Model Army, David Bowie, Bruce Hornsby & The Range, Eurythmics, Genesis and Paul Young.

Concert for Berlin

6.-8. Juni · Platz der Republik

Einlaß jeweils 16 Uhr   34188   ✳

Some speakers are directed toward the East. Thousands of teenagers like me gather at the barrier in front of the Brandenburg Gate to listen to our idols.

David Bowie doesn't forget his fans in the East: "We send our greetings to our friends on the other side of the Wall."

♪ We can be Heroes ♪

The authorities are not at all amused.

On the night of June 7th, we try to get as close as we can to the Brandenburg Gate. But the police force us back.

DAMNED PIGS!!

DOWN WITH THE WALL!!

Things gets out of hand.

The teenagers vent their anger.

I take some pictures.

COME HERE, BUSTER!

The Stasi take my film and check my ID.

158 teenagers are arrested.

I'm shocked by the police brutality.
I write a report about it and send it together with my unconfiscated photos to the TV show "Kontraste" in West Berlin.

couldn't believe, like being enchained, heard screa
the cops started running, as though
hunting, but they weren't the hunted
we were and they were the hunters!! We,
only wanted to listen to music in front of Bran
burg Gate, and were hunted toward the city center
like mad and grabbed everyone who wasn't
enough, and we ran as fast as we could
banged on trash cans, and we ran
across the Linden near the opera house an
seized the opportunity along with a few others
and escaped into a side street by the palace
to catch our breath and get away
from it all. I was totally out of breath, scared
my knees were shaking, my legs were heavy

But it never arrives.
The Stasi intercepted it.

Six weeks later, the Stasi pick me up at work.

When they search my apartment, they find all 179 prints of the Wall and the 35 rolls of film they came from.

They take me to the Stasi remand center "Hohenschönhausen."

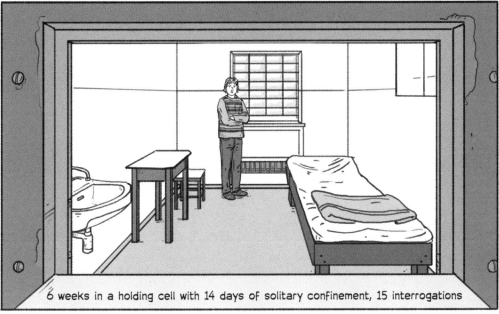

6 weeks in a holding cell with 14 days of solitary confinement, 15 interrogations

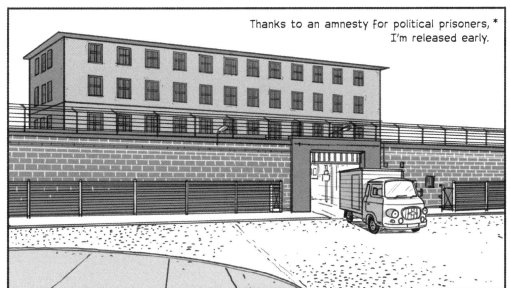

Thanks to an amnesty for political prisoners, *
I'm released early.

* The result of GDR president and party leader Erich Honecker's visit to West Germany in September 1987.

I apply for an exit visa. It's approved.
I have to leave the GDR by midnight on February 26, 1988.

As soon as I get to the West,
I take a look over the
colorful Wall into
the East.

THE END

74

DETLEF MATTHES' EXIT VISA

"We Can Be Heroes"

David Bowie

VOLKSPOLIZEI

[People's Police]

In 1987, the Wall had already been standing for 26 years. An entire generation had grown up in its shadows. In East and West, people were coming to terms with the concrete reality, which was much easier for those in the free and rich West than for the walled-in Easterners. But even here, many people had already made peace with the border and were trying to make the best of the circumstances at hand. They vacationed in other Eastern Bloc countries because the vast majority of East Germans were not allowed to travel to western nations. Generally only trustworthy party members and senior citizens were allowed to travel to the West. Seniors who stayed in the West saved the GDR pension payments. "Normal citizens" were not issued passports but had to wait until retirement age to get one. Teenagers in particular projected their unfulfilled desires onto the unreachable West. They strove to break free from their parents and the gray socialist reality, and sought role models on the other side of the Wall. Rock bands, film stars and western clothing played a major role in their lives. Those caught with such insignias of "western decadence" were often subjected to indoctrination and public defamation. Punks and hippies could also be found in the GDR, but they were often the victims of police and Stasi reprisals.

GDR leaders were highly suspicious of the unconventional performances of western rock and pop bands and their freedom and protest ideals. They feared losing control over the country's youth. But western radio (and later television) was also broadcast into the East, and kept teenagers well informed about the latest trends in the West. The news that David Bowie and several other famous bands would be playing in front of the Reichstag in West Berlin as part of the city's 750th anniversary celebration electrified crowds of teenagers in both East and West. Thousands of fans from throughout the GDR, including Detlef Matthes, gathered near the Wall by the Brandenburg Gate in the hopes of being able to hear bits and pieces of the music. The police responded with brutality, arresting dozens of fans and detaining them for hours under inhuman conditions.

Many teenagers eluded the state-ordered conformity through their outfits and musical tastes. More and more people became politically active. Beginning in the 1970s, oppositional groups sprouted up in the GDR, increasingly causing headaches for the ruling SED. First so-called "house circles" formed to discuss ideas for reforming socialism, to collect donations for detainees in Poland, and to translate oppositional papers from Polish and Czech. Then in the early-1980s, new groups began emerging to protest SED policies. The church provided a certain safe haven for peace, environmental, women's and human rights groups, which were cleverly impeding state and police access and winning over more and more critically-thinking people for their aims. They used western media to reach their audiences and enjoyed growing solidarity on their home soil. As their grassroots support continued to broaden, it became impossible for the Stasi to completely suppress the oppositional groups.

In terms of numbers, the largest oppositional group consisted of people who had applied for an exit visa to go to the West. They demanded their right to free movement, which did not exist in the GDR. Through demonstrative meetings on public squares – so-called "White Circles" – petitions, and their own groups of exit visa applicants, they became better and better organized. Although those who left the country or were detained weakened the potential for dissent, the success of their applications and protests motivated countless others who had remained silent until then to join in the demonstrations.

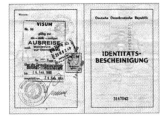

GDR Identity Card with a single-exit visa

During the autumn of 1989, the SED lost more and more control over the situation. Increasing numbers of people joined the mass rallies against the regime. November 9, 1989 was to become one of the most exhilarating days of the season. But for Jan Hildebrandt, who turned 18 on this day, it could not have started out more boring ...

ON LOCATION

For decades, the **BRANDENBURG GATE** was the symbol of the city's division. The Wall ran between the Gate and the Reichstag. Today a row of cobblestones marks the Wall's former route. The S-Bahn below the square in front of the Brandenburg Gate formerly linked the northern with the southern part of West Berlin, passing below the eastern part of the city without stopping. All of the stations in the East were closed

and were patrolled by armed transportation police. The entrances were closed and partially bricked up so those in East Berlin could not see that the West S-Bahn passed beneath East Berlin here.

White crosses at the edge of the Tiergarten at the corner of Ebert-, Scheidemann- and Dorotheenstrasse and along the Spree River behind the Reichstag pay tribute to those who lost their lives here at the border.

▶ **S- and U-Bahn station Brandenburger Tor**

A CHUNK OF THE BERLIN WALL

JAN HILDEBRANDT: My 18th Birthday

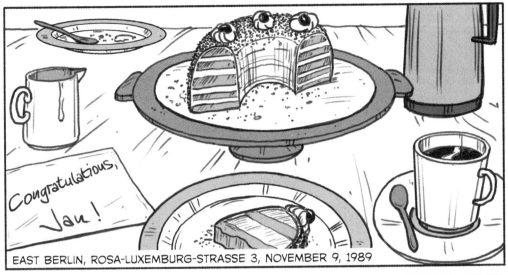

EAST BERLIN, ROSA-LUXEMBURG-STRASSE 3, NOVEMBER 9, 1989

It wasn't even 8 o'clock yet
and my 18th birthday was
already over.

My sister ELSKE

My best friend FRANK

My mother REGINE

I'll be in my room.

Put it over there.
I'll take care of it.

Some birthday party that was! The best part was the Coca-Cola my parents gave me.

What did you expect? Everybody wanted to get home to watch the news. You guys don't have a TV.

I know. Politics are more important than my birthday right now.

Dad should already be home from the "Democracy Now" meeting.

Hopefully they didn't arrest him ...

18 years / 18 cans

They wouldn't dare. Not after hundreds of thousands of us were at last week's rally on Alexanderplatz!

And everything we were yelling for: free elections, freedom of opinion, freedom to travel ... It was great!

RIING!

Know what else is gonna be great? When you get your driver's license!

Yeah! Having a car's kinda like being free, huh?

You can already drive. And if my dad's connections come through, you won't have to wait long at all.

Then we'll go as far as we can with my parents' Wartburg!

Meanwhile, my father had come home.

Friederike just called: She said the Wall's open! Are you coming with us to the West?

81

The six of us squeeze into our Wartburg and head for the border crossing at the Bornholmer Bridge. My uncle, who lives in the apartment above us, comes along.

At this hour it's usually dead as a doornail around here.

Because traffic isn't budging an inch, we youngsters get out and walk ahead.

We get really close to the barrier.

Thousands of us are waiting for something to happen.

The atmosphere is tense and brimming with anticipation.

Open the gate!

A handful of border guards are standing opposite a sea of people.

What are they going to do?

They've received conflicting orders from above and don't know what to do.

Let 'em out!

The commander has to decide on his own.

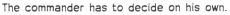

The people flood the border fortifications like a bursting dam.
There's no stopping them now.

The crowds cross the bridge
into West Berlin.

After being closed for 28 years, the gates in the Wall are suddenly wide open.

Friends separated by the Wall celebrate their reunion.

A baker hands out free rolls.

We can't find our parents in the never-ending sea of faces.

Suddenly we're in the West ...

... where we've never been before.

Because we look lost,
a friendly West Berliner offers to let
us use his phone.

We're here!

We call our relatives in West Berlin.

They pick us up in their car ...

... and show us all the hot spots:

THE VICTORY COLUMN

STRASSE DES
17. JUNI

THE MEMORIAL CHURCH

THE RADIO TOWER

Along the way we call home to our parents.

What! Come home???

But Dad, we're here in the West!

And now you're coming home!
You can go back after school tomorrow.
But you've got to go to the Brandenburg
Gate. That's where we just came from.

Our relatives bring us there before heading
home. They've got to get up early
the next morning.

Our parents could walk through the gate, but now it's closed again.

I just have to get a souvenir.

CHECKPOINT INVALIDENSTRASSE

We get home early in the morning.

Now *that's* what I call a birthday party!

THE END

Revolution!

DEMOKRATISCHER
A U F B R U C H

Jan Hildebrandt never imagined he would be spending his 18th birthday in West Berlin. While the construction of the Wall in 1961 was planned down to the minutest detail, its fall on November 9, 1989 was the result of absolute chaos. The SED dictatorship, which the Wall helped safeguard, was collapsing from within. The authorities were overwhelmed by the larger and larger protest rallies which had been taking place in numerous cities beginning in early-October. All across the country, people were organizing candlelight vigils and intercession prayers in churches such as the Gethsemanekirche in Prenzlauer Berg in Berlin. The oppositional initiatives that had emerged during the summer presented their platforms and debated openly with the people: Neues Forum (New Forum), Demokratie Jetzt (Democracy Now) and Demokratische Aufbruch (Democratic Awakening). The Social Democratic Party (SDP) was founded on October 7th, followed by the Green Party and the Green League in November.

At first the SED used massive police operations, arrests and penalty orders to try to gain the upper hand over the situation. But by October 9th at the latest, it became clear that the party's efforts were doomed. On this day, 70,000 people peacefully protested against the SED regime along the inner-city ring in Leipzig following the weekly prayer for peace in the Nikolaikirche. In light of the overwhelming number of protestors, the officer in charge ordered the armed police and military forces to remain on the sidelines. It was the first decisive victory for the peace movement. Following the resignation of the political leadership on October 18th and further protests, some 200,000 people gathered on Berlin's Alexanderplatz on November 4th for the largest free demonstration in the GDR to date.

Late on the afternoon of November 9th, the famous press conference which led to the fall of the Wall took place. While announcing new travel regulations, SED politburo member Günter Schabowski rather casually declared that every citizen of the GDR would be allowed to travel to the West. He failed to make it clear, however, that the new law actually applied to emigration regulations, for which an application had to be filed just like for visitations to the West. Upon being queried by western journalists, Schabowski announced that the new regulation was "effective immediately." West German news agencies picked up these statements and broadcast them on television back into the GDR. As a result, a rush of curious onlookers, including Jan Hildebrandt and his family, began to appear at the various border checkpoints. What no one suspected, however, was that the border guards stamped the ID card photos of the first people crossing into the West with an exit stamp in order to denaturalize them so they could not return to the GDR. But fortunately this never became reality. At 11:30 p.m., the officer in charge at the Bornholmer Strasse checkpoint could no longer

Günter Schabowski

hold back the crowds and opened the barriers to everyone. For the first time in 28 years, tens of thousands of people poured freely across the bridge into West Berlin. Later the same evening, the other border checkpoints followed suit. The entire city was in a state of ecstacy. Complete strangers from East and West fell into one another's arms and shed tears of joy. "Awesome!" was on the tip of everyone's tongue. The Wall was open!

The people of the GDR had fought for their political freedom and brought down the Wall on November 9th. While Berlin souvenir hunters transformed into "Mauerspechte" (Wall woodpeckers), who sold chunks of the Wall to tourists in front of the newly accessible Brandenburg Gate, the autumn awakening of 1989 forged ahead toward German reunification. On October 3, 1990, more than 40 years of German division officially ended. The remains of the Berlin Wall are now under monument protection and can be visited. Now they tell us stories from a time which is hardly imaginable ...

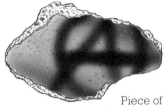

Piece of
the Berlin Wall

ON LOCATION

The former border checkpoint **BORN-HOLMER STRASSE** is now a completely normal bridge connecting the Berlin districts Prenzlauer Berg and Wedding. The S-Bahn station below the bridge used to be in the middle of the border area. S-Bahn trains connecting the northern and southern parts of West Berlin passed through it without stopping. On what is now the two easternmost tracks of the intercity railway, the East Berlin S-Bahn rode through the death strip, which was fortified by walls, barbed wire and dog runs. There was no connection to the S-Bahn circle line.

Remains of the Hinterland wall (interior wall) are visible on the northern side of the street. Memorial plaques pay witness to the location's history.

The **BERLINER MAUERWEG** (Berlin Wall Trail) passes directly by the former border checkpoint. The 160 km bicycle and footpath runs the entire length of where the Wall once stood and surrounded the former half-city of West Berlin. If you follow the Mauerweg signs across Norweger Strasse and the northern quarter, you will end up in the **MAUERPARK**.

▶ **S-Bahn station Bornholmer Strasse**

Selected bibliography

> Camphausen, Gabriele; Nooke, Maria: *Die Berliner Mauer*. Exhibition catalogue Berlin Wall Documentation Center. Michel Sandstein Verlag, Dresden 2003

> Dittfurth, Udo: *August 1961. S-Bahn und Mauerbau*. Verlag GVE, Berlin 2003

> Eisenfeld, Bernd; Engelmann, Roger: *13.8.1961: Mauerbau. Fluchtbewegung und Machtsicherung*. Edition Temmen, Bremen 2001

> Festschrift: *100 Jahre Lazarus-Kranken- und Diakonissenhaus 1865-1965*. Berlin 1965

> Gröschner, Annett; Messmer, Arwed: *Aus anderer Sicht/The Other View: Die frühe Berliner Mauer/The Early Berlin Wall*. Hatje Cantz Verlag, Ostfildern 2012

> Halbrock, Christian: *Weggesprengt. Die Versöhnungskirche im Todesstreifen der Berliner Mauer 1961-1985* (Sonderheft Horch und Guck Nr. 17/2008). Berlin 2008

> Hertle, Hans-Hermann: *Die Berliner Mauer/The Berlin Wall. Monument des Kalten Krieges/ Monument of the Cold War* (Bundeszentrale für politische Bildung; Nr.08). Bonn 2007

> Hertle, Hans-Hermann; Nooke, Maria u.a.: *Die Todesopfer an der Berliner Mauer 1961-1989*. Hg. v. Zentrum für Zeithistorische Forschung Potsdam und der Stiftung Berliner Mauer. Ch. Links Verlag, 2nd edition, Berlin 2009

> Kundt, Klaus; Sakowitz, Horst: *"Gleich kommt einer vom Dach!"*. BILD am SONNTAG, 1.8.1965, p. 9 (reproduction rights courtesy of BILD am SONNTAG)

> Müller, Bodo: *Faszination Freiheit. Die spektakulärsten Fluchtgeschichten*. Ch. Links Verlag, 4th edition, Berlin 2001

> Sälter, Gerhard; Schaller, Tina; Kaminsky, Anna (Hg.): *Weltende – Die Ostseite der Berliner Mauer. Mit heimlichen Fotos von Detlef Matthes* (publication of the Berlin Wall Foundation). Ch. Links Verlag, Berlin 2011

> Schülerinnen und Schüler des Abiturjahrgangs 1961 der Bertha-von-Suttner-Schule in Berlin-Reinickendorf: *Immer auf der Hut. Ost-Schüler in West-Berlin – Als die Mauer dazwischen kam*. Hg. v. Verlag Schleichers Buchhandlung, Berlin 2011

> *VEB Tourist Stadtplan Ost-Berlin*. 18th edition Berlin/Leipzig 1985. (reproduction rights courtesy of Weimarer Verlagsgesellschaft Ltd)

> Contemporary Witnesses Archives of the Berlin Wall Memorial Center

Newspaper article from page 55

BILD am SONNTAG, August 1, 1965:

At midnight sharp, little Günter donned a rope sling and courageously glided down a 140 meter long zipline into the abyss 25 meters below. Then came his mother. "I saw the death strip below me. When I saw the Wall, I thought: Now you've been saved!" The father was the last to roll into freedom – with a pulley made by a state-owned metalworking shop according to Holzapfel's plans. Upon arriving at a hotel, they drank a cognac to calm their nerves. Then they were off to bed. The overnight stay and breakfast were complimentary. The helpers were audacious enough to partially roll up the escape cable and throw it atop the Wall. The People's Police did not discover it until several hours later.

Heinz Holzapfel can hardly express his joy. "When I think about how we crawled along the roof in the pouring rain, light pouring out of a dormer window – apparently border guards lived there. But we had to take the chance." The Leipzig family could no longer bear the conditions in the Zone. "I realized that communist reality was totally different than the textbook ideology." This comes from a man who spent years explaining the SED* Central Committee's resolutions to his colleagues. After all, Heinz Holzapfel was considered a golden boy in the Zone: A trained carpenter, he joined the People's Police, where he attended officer's school. With the help of some scholarships, he completed his high school and studied at Karl-Marx-University for four years. "I was a convinced communist!" confesses the former SED functionary now. But the construction of the Wall filled him with doubts which continued to grow. Finally he decided to flee. Heinz Holzapfel looks optimistically into the future: He wants to establish his livelihood in Southern Germany on the basis of two patents which he had registered in West Berlin some time ago.

Photo caption (top): Heinz, Julia and son Günter Holzapfel wore these homemade "creeping socks" to avoid making any suspicious sounds on the roof of the "House of Ministries." They really thought of everything.

Photo caption (middle): Mr. Holzapfel used this skydiving book to prepare his son for the dangerous undertaking.

Photo caption (right): After the successful escape: A border policeman with a rifle over his shoulder pulls the cable over the Wall and back into the East.

Photo caption (below): Their first breakfast together on West Berlin territory: Now the Holzapfel family can forget about sedatives and all the excitement.

* SED = Sozialistische Einheitspartei (Socialist Unity Party) – the governing party of the German Democratic Republic.

The Authors

Susanne Buddenberg and **Thomas Henseler** studied design at the Fachhochschule Aachen and film at the Hochschule für Film und Fernsehen "Konrad Wolf" in Potsdam-Babelsberg. Upon completing their studies, they founded the company Zoom und Tinte Buddenberg und Henseler GbR, which specializes in film and illustration. Together they work in the fields of comics, illustration and storyboarding for film productions, television stations and advertising and event agencies. They also teach game design.

Thanks!

To our contemporary witnesses whose personal stories and trust in us made this project possible:
Jan Hildebrandt
Holzapfel family
Ursula Malchow
Detlef Matthes
Regina Thulesius (maiden name: Zywietz)

Our funder:
The Federal Foundation for the Reappraisal of the SED Dictatorship

Our consultants:
Dr. Christian Halbrock
Dr. Maria Nooke
Markus Pieper

Our supporters:
Willi Blöß
Miriamne Fields
Alexander Hembt
Torsten Meißner
Rick Minnich
Jakob Rössler
Andreas Rupprecht
Anna Schmelz
Johann Ulrich
and our friends and families

"**Grippingly told and professionally illustrated**"
Der Tagesspiegel

"**Entertaining and instructive**"
GDR Museum

"**Compelling story**"
Superillu

"**As thrilling as a detective story**"
STRAPAZIN

"**Teachers who are notoriously skeptical about comics absolutely must take a look at this book.**"
Berliner Zeitung

"**Also for adults, the drawings and dialogue make tangible everyday life in a dictatorship of the mind and what it meant to revolt against it.**"
Deutschlandradio

Grenzfall by Thomas Henseler and Susanne Buddenberg

GDR 1982, East Berlin: High school student Peter Grimm rebels against the dictatorship of the mind in a country which is suffocating him. Through the family of dissident Robert Havemann, he finds new friends and like-minded people who share his desire for freedom. He is expelled from school for his "moral character and attitude." But Peter remains faithful to his ideals: Together with his friends, he publishes the illegal newspaper "Grenzfall" (Borderline Case), which contains uncensored reports about social problems the authorities are trying to suppress at all costs. "Grenzfall" becomes an unofficial bestseller and is passed from hand to hand throughout the GDR.

 The Stasi eventually deploys its entire surveillance apparatus to stop the newspaper. A traitor infiltrates the inner circles of "Grenzfall," and supplies the Stasi with valuable information. A devastating blow to the "enemies of the state" begins ...

Made possible with the support of the Federal Foundation for the Reappraisal of the SED Dictatorship

ISBN: 978-3-939080-48-0
Paperback, 104 pages, German
14.95 Euros

Thomas Henseler · Susanne Buddenberg
Tunnel 57
Eine Fluchtgeschichte als Comic
112 Seiten · 26 Comic-Seiten und 29 Abbildungen im Text
ISBN 978-3-86153-721-2
9,90 € (D) · 10,20 € (A)

Anhand von Zeitzeugeninterviews, Originalfotos und Dokumenten haben die Comic-Autoren die Ereignisse um den legendären Fluchttunnel unter der Bernauer Straße im Jahr 1964 detailgetreu rekonstruiert und grafisch umgesetzt. Ein Beitrag zu den historischen Hintergründen weitet den Blick auf das Fluchtgeschehen, Interviews mit einem Fluchthelfer und seiner geflüchteten Freundin veranschaulichen die Ereignisse aus deren Perspektive. Ergänzende Materialien für den Schulunterricht vertiefen die Thematik.

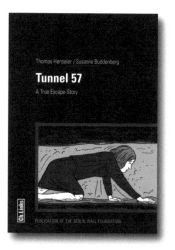

Thomas Henseler · Susanne Buddenberg
Tunnel 57
A True Escape-Story
32 Seiten, davon 26 Comic-Seiten
ISBN 978-3-86153-729-8
4,90 € (D) · 5,10 € (A)

This historical comic book is an escape helper's first person account of the construction of a tunnel beneath the divided city of Berlin in 1964: From the preparations on the West Berlin side, the digging of the 145 metre long tunnel into East Berlin, the tunnel opening and the successful escape on the first day, and the dramatic events of the second day which were to have grave consequences. Drawing on authentic interviews with the tunnel builders and refugees and original photographs and documents, writers and illustrators Thomas Henseler and Susanne Buddenberg recreate down to the last detail the dramatic events surrounding Tunnel 57.

Ch. Links Verlag
Schönhauser Allee 36
10435 Berlin
Telefon (030) 44 02 32 - 0
Fax (030) 44 02 32 - 29
mail@christoph-links-verlag.de
www.christoph-links-verlag.de

Ch.Links